Let's Imagine...

Let's Imagine ...

An orphan's life and the hope of adoption

Written By: Deneen Alexandrow Turner

Illustrated By: Ivanka Pikush

Endorsements

"Deneen Turner has been a leader in ministering to institutionalized orphans around the globe and helping resource families to adopt them for many years. I am so thankful she has brought the same passion and expertise that drives her ministry to helping children understand God's heart for the fatherless. There are precious few resources to help teach young children about orphan life or the hope that they can find through adoption. The beautiful illustrations and insightful writing in *Let's Imagine* help children identify with the desperate plight of the millions of orphans who live in institutions around the world and gives them ideas of how they can help right now. Whether you are a parent or you serve with children in ministry, I would highly recommend this book as a tool for talking to your children about adoption and educating them on their power to give aid in Jesus' name."

Rick Morton
Co-Author of *Orphanology*

"Let's Imagine. There was a time in my life when I really could not imagine the life of an orphan, but then I met Deneen Turner. Deneen was the first person to take me inside a little Ukrainian orphanage where my life would be changed forever and eighteen months later our family would bring home one of the little girls we met on that trip. Now Deneen has combined her writing skills and compassionate heart to help children understand the heart of our Father for children around the world. As a father and grandfather, I want to commend this book to you as a teaching tool for your children. As a pastor, I want to commend this book to you as a tool for the teaching ministry of your church. Just think what would happen if every church in America began to communicate these truths to children about children. Deneen has placed a valuable tool in our hands that could change the lives of children all across the world. **Let's Imagine** *that!*

"HopeHouse International® is one of the greatest ministries serving children in the world today. It is a ministry that is absolutely credible, God honoring, and worthy of the support of both individuals and churches. Only eternity will truly reveal the impact of this ministry and the lives of orphans that have been changed as a result."

Rick White
Sr. Pastor, The People's Church, Franklin, TN
Board Member, HopeHouse International®

Published by Gifts-that-Give Publishing. No part of this book may be reproduced
or transmitted in any form or by any means, electronic or mechanical, including
photocopying, recording, or by any information storage and retrieval system,
without written permission from the publisher.

For information address Gifts-that-Give Publishing
c/o HopeHouse International®
P.O. Box 1097, Franklin, TN 37065
Printed in the United States of America

Library of Congress Cataloging-in-Publication Data is available.
ISBN 978-0-615-75784-1
First Edition

Summary: By engaging in *Let's Imagine*, children better understand the realities
of orphan life in many parts of the world and how we can respond to their
hopelessness through involvement with adoption.

To order *Let's Imagine,* visit www.hopehouseinternational.org/gifts-that-give

Let's Imagine...
is dedicated to my son, Drew.
He is my inspiration.

"You can actually *see* hope when
you *give* hope to someone else."
— *Drew Turner*

Let's Imagine
Just Imagine
How others might be

And maybe God's blessings
Yourself, you will see

Think About

The time you spend with your mom and dad is very special.

Your home is filled with beautiful colors and is always cozy and warm.

You feel safe when you are with your parents,
because **they love you so much.**

Let's Imagine

You do not have a family or a home.

You live in a big building with grey walls and cold floors.

In the winter you always feel cold.

In that building, **you never feel safe.**

Think About

You have a beautiful bedroom.

In your room you have a bed, a closet full of clothes and shoes, lots of books, and tubs filled with toys.

You have everything you need.

Let's Imagine

You do not have your own room, clothes, shoes, books, or toys.

You have to share everything with many other kids.

Not one thing is your very own.

Think About

When you smell your mom's cooking down the hall, you get excited about meal times.

Meal times around the table are filled with laughter and fun.

You feel loved.

Let's Imagine

You do not get a choice of what to eat throughout the day.

Meal times are lonely.

There is very little food.

Most of the time . . . **you are hungry.**

Think About

Your mom and dad tell you many times how much they love you.

Your birthday and all your important days are a big celebration!

Because you are so special, **your parents celebrate YOU!**

Let's Imagine

No one celebrates your birthday.

You are not treated with kindness.

You do not feel loved.

You feel like you do not belong to anyone.

Think About

Your mom and dad take care of you when you get hurt
or when you are sick.

**They are always there to help you
and make you feel better.**

Let's Imagine

You do not have a mom and a dad . . . even though you wish for them every day of your life.

Your heart hurts because you want to be held, hugged, and loved . . . but there is no one to do those things for you.

You just keep hoping that one day a mom and dad will come *just* for you and make you a part of their family.

You feel so alone.

Think About

The scenes that you **imagined** are very **real** for children in many parts of the world.

There are children that have no homes and no parents. Many of them live in the concrete buildings you imagined. These places are called orphanages.

Most children in orphanages live every day lonely, sad, and scared of what might happen to them.

So what can families do to help?

Let's Imagine

A person with lots of love travels to an orphanage, brings a child home and makes them a part of their family. This is called "**adoption**."

There may also be a person who wants to help a child in an orphanage, but they may not be able to adopt. This person *also* has lots of love, so *they* choose to **help other families adopt!**

Whether a person **adopts** a child or **helps** another family adopt, they are **both** giving that child a family to love them.

Let's Imagine
Just Imagine
How others might be

Then maybe in a child
Their needs you will see

Now We Can Know

When children from orphanages are adopted,
they no longer have to imagine, and neither do you . . .

They now have a mom and a dad who love them.

They are **not alone any more.**

Now We Can Know

They live in a beautiful home.

They have their own bed and lots of books, toys, and clothes.

At home, they feel **safe and warm.**

Now We Can Know

There is plenty of food at meal times.

The refrigerator is full of snacks, drinks, fruits, vegetables, and ice-cream!

They are **not hungry anymore.**

Now We Can Know

They live in a colorful world of family, friends, celebrations, birthday parties, activities, hugs and kisses, and most importantly . . . **God's love.**

Because of people with lots of love, **adopted children will never live in that dark and scary world again.**

Just Imagine
Let's Imagine
When people do care

We all see that love
Is the best gift to share

About The Author

Deneen Alexandrow Turner is a graduate of Baylor University and former professional singer for the Billy Graham Evangelistic Association from 1987-2004. She is of Ukrainian descent and speaks fluent Russian. Deneen and Ukrainian native, Yuri Yakovlyev, have been partners since 1990 ministering to orphans throughout Ukraine by facilitating orphan care mission trips for teams from the U.S. They continue to do so today.

In the year 2000, Deneen and Yuri co-founded HopeHouse International® in order to help orphans become adopted by Ukrainian Christian couples who raise them in their own country. HopeHouse International® has since expanded into addition Eastern European countries. **www.hopehouseinternational.org**

Over the last two decades, Deneen has been actively working with orphan issues, orphan care missions, and international in-country adoptions. She is Co-Founder and President of HopeHouse International®, and resides in Franklin, Tennessee with her husband, Mark, and their son Drew.

About The Illustrator

Ivanka Pikush, born in 1990, is the daughter of HopeHouse International® Co-Founder, Yuri Yakovlyev. Ivanka lives in Kiev, Ukraine. She has been painting since the age of three and her work has been displayed in children's art exhibitions all over Europe. She has received the highest awards in national art competitions throughout her elementary and high school years of education.

Ivanka has been involved in orphan care with HouseHouse International® since she was a young girl and has served for many years on HopeHouse International® mission trips as an English speaking interpreter.

Ivanka graduated Kiev State Institute of Decorative and Applied Art and Design with a major in monumental painting. In addition to painting when commissioned, Ivanka enjoys a career in interior design.

About HopeHouse International®

HopeHouse International® exists so that orphans can become adopted by Christian couples within their own countries. Adequate housing is a barrier for many citizens and in most countries it is a government prerequisite for adoption. HopeHouse International® enables adoptions by addressing adequate housing needs which result in three or more children being given a family and a future.

HopeHouse International® also facilitates ministry opportunities through orphan care mission trips and volunteer building teams.

For more information, visit us at **www.hopehouseinternational.org.**